DINOSA ROAR
and FRIENDS!

Turn the pages to meet the dinosaurs.
Read the facts and then turn to the back
of the book for a roar-some quiz.

See if you can spot Dinosaur Squeak on every page!

Can you say all the dinosaur names?
Look out for the pronunciation
guides at the bottom
of every page.

MACMILLAN CHILDREN'S BOOKS

The king of the dinosaurs, Dinosaur Roar,
Had a roar that no creature could ever ignore.

Roar is a
Tyrannosaurus rex.
He has **teeth** the
size of **bananas!**

Roar walks
on his two
hind legs.

Roar's arms
are **too short**
to reach
his mouth.

Tyrannosaurus rex
Tie-RAN-oh-sore-us rex

Dinosaur Honk was too noisy by far.
The *Parasaurolophus* honked like a car!

Honk, the *Parasaurolophus* makes a loud **noise** by using the **crest** on her head.

Honk has a **wide**, **flat** mouth that looks like a duck's beak.

Honk usually walks on **four** legs, but sometimes walks on **two**.

Parasaurolophus
Pa-ra-saw-ROL-off-us

The kind *Oviraptor* named Dinosaur Flap
Was so nervous, she couldn't sit down for a nap.

Flap, the *Oviraptor* has a distinctive, **feathery** tail.

Flap has a **toothless beak**, like a parrot.

Flap sometimes sits on her nest to **protect** her eggs, like a bird.

Oviraptor
OH-vee-RAP-tor

Dinosaur Whizz loved to run and to chase;
The swift *Coelophysis* would win every race!

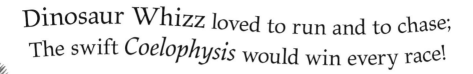

Whizz, the *Coelophysis* balances herself with her **long tail**.

Whizz's long back legs help her **run fast**.

Whizz has three **grasping claws** on each hand.

 Coelophysis **Seel-OH-fie-sis**

The *Ankylosaurus* called Dinosaur Bash
Had a club on his tail that he loved to THRASH!

Bash, the *Ankylosaurus* has a **club** on his tail the size of a **football**!

Bash's body is covered in **armour**, like a crocodile.

Bash's name, *Ankylosaurus*, means '**fused lizard**'.

 Ankylosaurus
An-KIE-loh-SORE-us

The clumsiest creature to wander the track
Was the young *Stegosaurus,* Dinosaur Whack.

Whack, the *Stegosaurus* has two rows of bony **plates** along her back.

Whack moves **slowly** and eats **plants**.

Whack has four **spikes** at the end of her tail.

Stegosaurus
STEG-oh-SORE-us

The huge *Diplodocus* called Dinosaur Munch
Had a tummy that never felt full after lunch.

Munch, the *Diplodocus* eats **leaves** from trees and soft plants.

Munch has a **long** tail, like a whip!

Diplodocus
DIP-low-DOCK-us

Deep in the forest, far from the swamp,
Lived a grumpy *Triceratops*, Dinosaur Stomp.

Stomp, the *Triceratops* has **three horns** on his head.

Stomp has a **large frill** around his neck.

Stomp has feet like an **elephant**.

Triceratops
Tri-SERRA-tops

The naughtiest dinosaur anyone knew,
Was the sneaky *Deinonychus*, Dinosaur Boo.

Boo, the *Deinonychus* can **leap** in the air, like a kangaroo!

Boo's long, stiff tail helps him to **balance** when he runs.

Boo has a big, hooked **claw** on the inside of each foot.

Deinonychus
Die-NON-i-kuss

The scariest monster to wander the map
Was the mean *Spinosaurus*, Dinosaur Snap.

Snap, the *Spinosaurus* has a **huge sail** on his back.

Snap has **powerful** jaws and sharp, **pointed** teeth, like a crocodile.

Snap has **large** feet and **wades** in the water, looking for **fish**.

Spinosaurus
SPINE-oh-SORE-us

The small *Compsognathus* called Dinosaur Squeak
Just could not be heard when she tried to speak.

Squeak, the *Compsognathus* is one of the **smallest** dinosaurs. She is about the size of a **chicken**!

Squeak has very **big eyes**.

Squeak is **bipedal**, which means she walks on **two** legs.

Did you find Squeak hiding on every page?

Compsognathus
Komp-sog-NATH-us

DINOSAUR QUIZ

Point to the dinosaurs on the opposite page that answer the questions below. If you get stuck, look through the book to find the answers!

1. Who is the king of all the dinosaurs?

2. Which dinosaur has two rows of bony plates along its back?

3. Where is the dinosaur with a very long neck?

4. Which dinosaur is armour-plated?

5. Can you find the fastest dinosaur?

6. Who is the smallest dinosaur?

7. Which dinosaur has three horns?

8. Who makes a noise like a car?

9. Who can leap in the air like a kangaroo?

10. Can you find the dinosaur with a sail on its back?

11. Where is the dinosaur who sits on a nest?

**DINOSAUR
ROAR!**
The Tyrannosaurus rex

**DINOSAUR
STOMP!**
The Triceratops

**DINOSAUR
HONK!**
The Parasaurolophus

**DINOSAUR
BOO!**
The Deinonychus

**DINOSAUR
BASH!**
The Ankylosaurus

**DINOSAUR
SQUEAK!**
The Compsognathus

**DINOSAUR
WHIZZ!**
The Coelophysis

**DINOSAUR
MUNCH!**
The Diplodocus

**DINOSAUR
FLAP!**
The Oviraptor

**DINOSAUR
SNAP!**
The Spinosaurus

**DINOSAUR
WHACK!**
The Stegosaurus

Answers: 1. Roar 2. Whack 3. Munch 4. Bash 5. Whizz 6. Squeak 7. Stomp 8. Honk 9. Boo 10. Snap 11. Flap

I celebrated World Book Day 2022 with this gift from my local bookseller and Macmillan Children's Books.

Have you read all these wonderful stories?

WORLD BOOK DAY

World Book Day's mission is to offer every child and young person the opportunity to read and love books by giving you the chance to have a book of your own.

To find out more, and for fun activities including our monthly book club, video stories and book recommendations visit **worldbookday.com**.

World Book Day is a charity funded by publishers and booksellers in the UK and Ireland.

World Book Day is also made possible by generous sponsorship from National Book Tokens and support from authors and illustrators.